Making Friends

1956

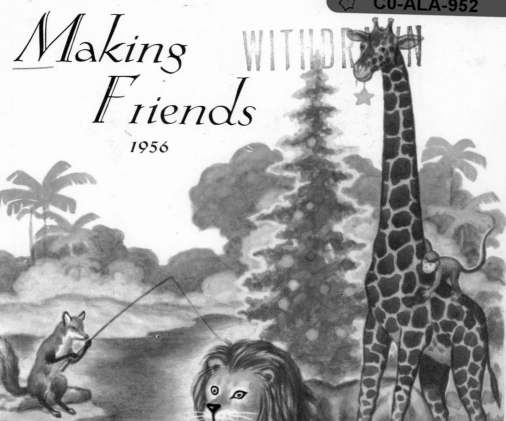

Bernice E. Leary
Edwin C. Reichert
Mary K. Reely

J. B. Lippincott Company · Chicago · Philadelphia · New York

The Editors

Bernice E. Leary, Curriculum Consultant, Madison, Wisconsin, Public Schools.

Edwin C. Reichert, Head of the Department of Education, Lake Forest College, Lake Forest, Illinois.

Mary K. Reely, formerly Chief of the Book Selection Department, Wisconsin Library Commission.

Illustrations

Library of Congress
Catalog Card Number: 53-6767

Gregory Orloff

Titles in the TIME TO READ Series

Making Friends
Skipping Along
Finding Favorites
Helping Others
Sailing Ahead
Moving Forward

ACKNOWLEDGMENTS

For permission to use copyrighted material, grateful acknowledgment is made to the following authors and publishers:

About Charlie. By Inez Hogan. Taken from *About Charlie*, copyright, 1950, by Inez Hogan, and published by E. P. Dutton & Company, Inc., New York.

Animal's Christmas Tree. By Rose L. Hardy and Geneva J. Hecox. From *Good Companions—Comrades*. Used by special permission of the authors and Newson & Company, publishers.

Bad. By Dorothy Aldis. From *Here, There, and Everywhere* by Dorothy Aldis. Used by special permission of the author and G. P. Putnam's Sons, publishers.

The Bed from *The Tiger and the Rabbit*. By Pura Belpre. Copyright by Houghton Miffllin Company. Used by special permission of the author and publishers.

A Day In A Cowboy's Life. From *Tenggren's Cowboys and Indians* by Kathryn and Byron Jackson. Copyright 1948 by Simon and Schuster, Inc., and Artists and Writers Guild, Inc. Used by permission.

Grown-up People. By Dorothy Aldis. From *Here, There, and Everywhere* by Dorothy Aldis. Used by special permission of the author and G. P. Putnam's Sons, publishers.

Hello and Good-bye. By James Steel Smith. Used by special permission of the author, and Jack and Jill, publishers.

A House for a Mouse. From *Chatterly Squirrel* and Other Animal Stories by Jane Werner, copyright 1950 by Simon and Schuster, Inc., and Artists and Writers Guild, Inc. Used by permission.

How They Walk. By Grace Olin Jordan. Used by special permission of the author.

Kitten Talk. By Clara Ellen Spelman. Used by special permission of the author and Jack and Jill, publishers.

The Little Cowboy. By Margaret Wise Brown. Reprinted with alterations, by permission of the publisher, William R. Scott, Inc., from *The Little Cowboy* by Margaret Wise Brown.

The Little Turtle. By Vachel Lindsay. Used by special permission of The Macmillan Company, publishers.

Littlest Cowboy. By Inez Hogan. Taken from *About the Littlest Cowboy* by Inez Hogan, copyright, 1951, by Inez Hogan, and published by E. P. Dutton & Company, Inc., New York.

The Mitten Song. By Marie Louise Allen. Used by special permission of the author.

The Moon. By Frances Gibson. Used by special permission of the author and Highlights for Children, Inc., Columbus, Ohio.

Mrs. Goose's Rubbers. By Miriam Clark Potter. From Child Study Association: *Read to Me Story Book*. Copyright, 1947, by Thomas Y. Crowell Company. Reprinted by permission of the publisher.

My Puppy. By Verna Hills. Copyright, 1945, by Story Parade, Inc. Reprinted by permission.

Our Clock. By Florence Eakman. Used by special permission of the author and Jack and Jill, publishers.

Pets in School. By Rebecca Caudill. From *Schoolhouse in the Woods* by Rebecca Caudill. Used by special permission of

3

Contents

Around the Year 111

At Our House 185

Cowboys

A Day In A Cowboy's Life

Right early in the morning is
　　The time that I like best,
I wash as quickly as I can
　　And hurry to get dressed.

I help the cook to build the fire
　　And put the kettles on.
Before he calls the rest to eat . . .
　　MY breakfast is all gone.

I saddle up my pony then,
    And ride around the place.
When tumbleweeds are blowing,
    I can have a dandy race.

Next I shoot a lot of Injuns
    And some outlaws, and a bear
And a coyote and a puma . . .
    If they happen to be there.

I go riding to the prairie,
    Where the sage and cactus grow,
To look for grazing antelope
    Or a herd of buffalo.

I round up straying cattle
    And I brand and notch a calf.
That isn't nearly all I do . . .
    It's even less than half!

I repair and paint the fences
  And I chop a lot of logs,
And I count a lot of tunnels
  Of a lot of prairie dogs.

But I'd get a lot more finished,
  If they didn't have a rule
That all cowboys turning seven
  Have to spend the day in school.

Kathryn and Byron Jackson

The Littlest Cowboy

Corky's grandfather was a
cowboy. His father was a cowboy.
And Corky was born on a ranch.

When he was only one year
old, Corky had a birthday party.
There was one candle on his
cake. And all the cowboys on
the ranch came to the ranch
house and brought presents.

They put a cowboy hat on
Corky's head and said, "Now
you're a cowboy. You're the
littlest cowboy." Then they sang
a cowboy birthday song:

> "The littlest cowboy—
>   Yippi ai yi!
>   He'll be the biggest
>   Bye and bye."

Corky could not talk when he
was one year old, but he could
laugh. And he did.

When Corky was two years old, he had another party. This time he had two candles on his cake. And all the cowboys came to the ranch house to bring presents for Corky.

The best present of all was a
cowboy shirt and a scarf. The
cowboys put them on Corky.
The shirt was blue, the scarf
was red. They put the hat on
Corky's head. Then the biggest
cowboy said, "Corky's two years
old today." And all the cowboys
sang:

"Yippi-ai-ay! Yippi-ai-ay!
The littlest cowboy is two today."

Corky could talk a little when
he was two. He shouted,

"Yippi! Yippi!
Corky cowboy!
Corky ride
CORKY RIDE!"

15

"Right," said Daddy. "Corky can ride." And Corky had his first ride on Daddy's big horse. He sat in front of his daddy.
Daddy cried,

"Yippi-ai-ay, away away—
Corky is two years old today."

And Corky cried,

"Yippi! Yippi!
Corky cowboy!
Corky ride
Corky ride!"

It wasn't long before Corky had a third birthday. This time he had three candles on his cake. And all the cowboys on the ranch came to the ranch house to celebrate.

They brought a little pair of cowboy chaps.

They put the chaps on Corky. Then they began to sing:

"Happy birthday, ki-yi!
Happy birthday, ki-ay!
The lit-tl-est cowboy
Is three today."

Corky could talk very well now. So he said, "Thank you. Now I'm a real cowboy."

"You sure are," said all the cowboys, "but you're still the littlest cowboy."

After Corky was three, he grew and grew. Soon he was four.

The cowboys came to the house again to celebrate Corky's birthday. They had a party, just like last year, and the year before, and the year before that.

They gave Corky a pair of cowboy boots for his fourth birthday and they said, "Now, Corky, you're a cowboy from head to foot. But you are still the littlest cowboy."

"Thanks," said Corky. And he
put on his new cowboy boots
and hopped around in them,
singing:

"Cowboy boots and chaps and
    hat,
Cowboy shirt and scarf. And
    that
Makes a cowboy outfit. So
I'm a COWBOY from head
    to toe."

That was a wonderful birthday.
Corky had the whole cowboy
outfit now. But he still didn't
have a gun. And he didn't have
something else a cowboy needs
too.

At last Corky was five years old. He didn't know what was going on so early in the morning of his birthday.

As soon as he woke up, even before he was dressed, Corky ran to the kitchen. His mother was baking a cake. He shouted, "I'm five! I'M FIVE!"

"Happy birthday," said Mother. "There's a present for you in your father's room."

Corky ran to his father's room. There he found a whole new cowboy outfit. "Yipeee!" shouted Corky. And he got into his new outfit as fast as he could and ran back to the kitchen.

"Well," said Corky's mother.
"You look fine. Daddy and I
thought you needed a new outfit.
You've outgrown the things the
cowboys gave you when you
were little."

"Where are the cowboys now?" asked Corky. "Don't they know it's my birthday?"

"Wait and see," said Mother.

"Maybe they have forgotten," said Corky. "I'll go outside. When they see my new cowboy outfit, they will remember."

But when Corky went outside there was not a cowboy in sight, not even his father.

Corky sat on the corral fence.
They have forgotten about my
birthday, he thought.

Then suddenly he heard a
song:

>"Yippi-ai-ay!
>It's Corky's birthday."

Into the corral rode all the
cowboys.

>They twirled their lassos,
>Rode bucking steers,
>They raced and they roped
>And shouted their cheers:
>"Happy birthday and joy
>To our little cowboy.
>Yippi-ai-ay!
>He's five today."

Corky was so happy he nearly
cried. But cowboys don't cry. So
Corky yelled. He made believe
that the fence was a horse and
he was riding it. And he
shouted:

"Yippi-ai-ay, away, away!
Riding a rodeo race today.
BANG! goes the gun—
YIPeeee, I won!"

Corky's father came over to
the fence. "Happy birthday, son.
That's a fine horse you're
riding."

"But it's only make-believe,"
said Corky. "Is the birthday
rodeo all over? Why are all the
cowboys going into the barn?"

"Let's find out," said his
father.

When Corky and his father
went into the barn, they saw
the cowboys standing around a
stall. They were looking down
at something.

"It was born today," said one
cowboy.

"On Corky's birthday," said another.

"A cowboy sure needs one."

"Can't get along without it."

"Guess he came 'special for Corky."

"Reckon that's Corky's birthday present."

"What is it?" asked Corky.

The cowboys moved away, and he saw a little colt.

"For ME?" he asked.

"He is your colt, son," said Corky's father.

"Gee," said Corky. "Ge-e-e-e-e-e . . ."

Corky's father explained that the colt was too young to ride yet. "He is only a baby now, but colts grow faster than boys.

When you are six, Corky, your colt will be as big as his mother. Then you can ride him."

Corky thought he could never wait a whole year.

"I'm going to name my colt Surprise," said Corky, "because that's what he is, a wonderful surprise."

Corky watched his little
Surprise colt try to stand up on
his wobbly legs. He laughed
when the colt wobbled over to
his mother to drink milk.

When the colt was old enough
to eat other food, Corky fed him
sugar and apples and carrots.
Every day Corky went to the
barn and called his colt.

"Surprise, Surprise,
I have a surprise for you."

Then—Corky had another birthday. This time he was six years old.

And do you know what the cowboys gave Corky on his sixth birthday? . . . A GUN and a holster to carry it in.

Not a real gun, of course. But it looked just like a real gun. And it went Bang! Bang! just like a real gun.

Now Corky was six and his colt, Surprise, was big enough to ride. So—

He rode his horse
And toted his gun.
He rode and he roped
And he had lots of fun.

He pulled out his gun
And he went, Bang! BANG!
He rode over the ranch
And sometimes he sang,

"I'm the littlest cowboy,
Yippi-ai-ay,
But I'll be the biggest
Cowboy someday."

Inez Hogan

30

Ridin' Herd

Cow heads and cow heads
Move across the plain,
Eating all the prairie grass,
Eating all the grain.
Cowboys on ponies
Ride out . . . and then
All cows of all kinds
Come this way again.
Red cows, white cows,
Cows everywhere.
Running cows, walking cows,
Cows that just stare.
Brown cows, tan cows,
Cows red and white.
Cow horns and cow tails
Move out of sight.

Kathryn and Byron Jackson

The Little Cowboy

Once upon a time in the far wild west, there were two cowboys.

One cowboy was a BIG COW-
BOY (BIG AS A MAN). And
the other cowboy was a very
little cowboy (knee high to a
grasshopper).

One had LARGE BOOTS. One
had little boots. One had a BIG
LASSO. One had a little lasso.
And they both had BIG HATS.

One had a BIG LOW VOICE.
One had a high little voice. And
they both sang cowboy songs.

They lived in two ranch houses
right near each other.

One cowboy had a BIG
BLACK AND WHITE PONY
that ate sugar from his hand.
And the other cowboy had a
little black and white pony
that ate sugar from his hand.

One day just as the sun came
up, there were two terrible clouds
of dust far out across the plains.
The cows were running away.

So the BIG COWBOY threw
his BIG LASSO and caught his
BIG PONY and galloped away
out over the plains after his
BIG COWS. The little cowboy
threw his little lasso, got on his
little pony and galloped away
out over the plains after his
little cows.

And as the BIG COWBOY
rode along he sang:

"I'VE TRAVELED UP, I'VE
   TRAVELED DOWN,
I'VE TRAVELED THIS WIDE
   WORLD ALL AROUND.
I'VE LIVED IN THE CITY,
I'VE LIVED IN TOWN,
AND I'VE GOT THIS MUCH
   TO SAY . . ."

And the little cowboy sang:

"Give me a great big horse
And a great big plain.
I'll go punching cows today."

Then the BIG COWBOY
had a BIG ROUND UP.

And the little cowboy had a little round up.

And when the BIG COW-BOY'S cows were all rounded up with a fence around them he headed for home. And when the little cowboy's cows were all rounded up with a fence around them, he headed for home.

They both headed for home,
just as the sun went down.
And the BIG COWBOY sang
in his GREAT BIG VOICE:

"I'VE TRAVELED UP, I'VE
    TRAVELED DOWN,
 I'VE TRAVELED THIS WIDE
    WORLD ALL AROUND.
 I'VE LIVED IN CITY, I'VE
    LIVED IN TOWN,
 AND I'VE THIS MUCH TO
    SAY . . ."

And the little cowboy sang in
his little high voice:

"Give me a great big horse
 And a great big plain,
 For I'm punching cows today."

37

And when they were almost home, the BIG COWBOY galloped up to his BIG RANCH HOUSE, and threw his TEN-GALLON HAT into the air, jumped off his horse, and tied him to a post.

And the little cowboy galloped up to his little ranch house, and threw his one-gallon hat into the air, jumped off his horse and tied him to a post.

Then they rubbed down their horses, and bedded down their horses, and gave them their supper.

Just as the stars came out they went into their ranch houses and closed the doors behind them.

And the BIG COWBOY
reached for his BIG FRYING
PAN and cooked himself a BIG
BEEF STEAK.

And the little cowboy reached
for his little frying pan and
cooked himself a little beef steak.

And the BIG COWBOY sang
to the moon in his GREAT
BIG VOICE. And the little
cowboy sang to the moon in his
little high voice. And they both
sang:

"I rode a great big horse
All around a great big plain.
I've been punching cows today."

Margaret Wise Brown

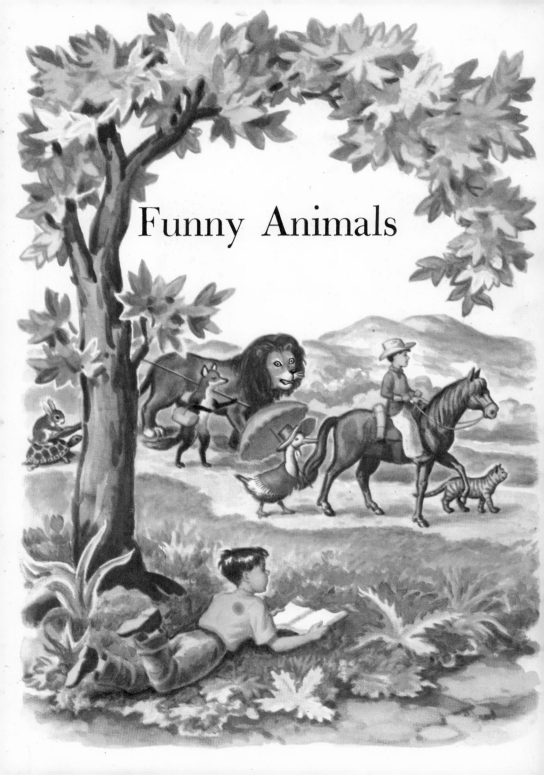

Funny Animals

The Little Turtle

There was a little turtle.
He lived in a box.
He swam in a puddle.
He climbed on the rocks.

He snapped at a mosquito.
He snapped at a flea.
He snapped at a minnow.
And he snapped at me.

He caught the mosquito.
He caught the flea.
He caught the minnow.
But he didn't catch me.

Vachel Lindsay

The Bed

There was once a little old woman who had a little boy. She brought him up under an old-fashioned bed.

But when the bed squeaked, the little boy was afraid and cried, "Boo, Hoo!" "Don't cry, little boy," said the little old woman. "It's only the sound of this old-fashioned bed."

Then the little old woman
bought a little dog, and gave it
to the little boy for company.

But when the bed squeaked,
the dog barked, "Bow, Wow."

And the boy cried, "Boo, Hoo!"

And the little old woman ran
to them and said, "Don't bark,
little dog. Don't cry, little boy.
It's only the sound of this old-
fashioned bed."

Then the little old woman
bought a little cat and gave it
to the boy and the dog for
company.

But when the bed squeaked,
the cat said, "Miaow, Miaow."

The dog barked, "Bow, Wow."

The boy cried, "Boo, Hoo."

And the little old woman ran
to them and said, "Don't miaow,
little cat. Don't bark, little dog.
Don't cry, little boy. It's only
the sound of this old-fashioned
bed."

Then the little old woman
bought a little mouse and gave
it to the boy and the dog and
the cat for company.

But when the bed squeaked,
the mouse cried, "Eek, Eek."

The cat said, "Miaow, Miaow."
The dog barked, "Bow, Wow."
The boy cried, "Boo, Hoo."
And the little old woman ran
to them and said, "Don't
squeak, little mouse. Don't
miaow, little cat. Don't bark,
little dog. Don't cry, little
boy. It's only the sound of this
old-fashioned bed."

Then the little old woman
bought a little pig, and gave it
to the boy and the dog and the
cat and the mouse for company.

But when the bed squeaked,
the pig grunted, "Oink! Oink!"

And the little old woman ran
to them and said, "Don't grunt,
little pig. Don't squeak, little
mouse. Don't miaow, little cat.
Don't bark, little dog. Don't cry,
little boy. It's only the sound of
this old-fashioned bed."

Then one day her little old
man came home and lay down
to rest on the old-fashioned bed.

But when the bed squeaked,
he cried, "Ah, Meeeeeeeee."

The pig grunted, "Oink! Oink!"

The mouse squeaked, "Eek,
Eek."

The cat said, "Miaow, Miaow."

The dog barked, "Bow, Wow."

The boy cried, "Boo, Hoo."

And the little old woman ran
to them and said, "Don't
grumble, old man. Don't grunt,
little pig. Don't squeak, little
mouse. Don't miaow, little cat.
Don't bark, little dog. Don't cry,
little boy. It's only the sound of
this old-fashioned bed."

Just then the old bed broke
down!

And the old man fell out.

And it hurt the little pig.

And it pinched the little
mouse.

And it scratched the little cat.

But the little dog was not
hurt.

And the little boy was saved.

And the little old woman was so
very brave that she just sat on
the floor and laughed and
laughed.

Pura Belpre

A House for a Mouse

One day Mrs. Mouse looked around her old shoe house. And she sighed a little sigh.

"My, there are so many children here. I don't know what to do," said she.

"Then I will leave home," said Freddy Mouse.

"And I will leave home," said Teddy Mouse.

"And I will leave home," said Reddy Mouse.

"We will all leave home. We will go out into the world to seek our fortunes," they said. And they kissed their mother good-by.

So out into the world went Freddy and Teddy and Reddy Mouse. They all started off to seek their fortunes. And to find new homes for themselves, of course.

Well, they traveled along. They came to a farm, with a big white house and a big red barn, and a big corn crib beside the barn. It was full of yellow corn.

Reddy Mouse found a hole in the corn crib. And he peeked in. He saw the heaps of corn. And all around the barnyard he saw oats and wheat and grass seeds— wonderful food for a small, hungry mouse.

"This is the place for me," said Reddy Mouse. So, with a wave of his paw, off he went into the corn crib. And Reddy became a happy farm mouse. He had found his fortune.

On went Freddy and Teddy Mouse. Soon they reached the big farm house. Teddy Mouse found a mouse-sized hole in the farm house wall. He peeked in. Sniff! sniff! sniff! Something smelled wonderful! He followed his nose to the kitchen. There, oh my! There were cheeses, and jellies and cakes and pies. The kitchen was full of things to eat!

"This is the place for me," said Teddy Mouse. So Teddy became a happy house mouse. He had found his fortune, too.

On went Freddy Mouse, all
by himself.

"I don't want to be a farm
mouse," said Freddy to himself.
"And I don't want to be a house
mouse. I want lots of people
around. I want light and music
and voices!"

So Freddy walked on and on.
Soon he came to a big building.
Lots of people were going in.
From the windows of the
building, high above Freddy's
head, lights were shining down.
They were yellow and green
and red and blue. And through
the open door he heard beautiful
music.

"Oh!" said Freddy. "Lights and music and lots of people! This is the place for me!"

So Freddy found a mouse-sized hole. And in he went. There was dark red carpeting on the floors. And the great windows shone like a sky full of stars.

"This is the place for me," said Freddy.

So Freddy became a happy church mouse. He sat in his mouse hole and looked out at the lights and people. And he wiggled his nose and said, "I have found my fortune, too."

Jane Werner

Tim Tadpole and the Great Bullfrog

Once there was a small pond at the edge of a wood. In the winter time this pond was very still, but in the spring time these sounds came from the pond.

"Sing—sing—sing—sing!" trilled the tiny Peeper Frogs.

"Jump—come jump—and jump!" croaked the Great Bullfrog.

But there was someone who lived in this pond who could neither sing nor jump and this was a small tadpole named Tim. All day long and all night long Tim Tadpole would listen and listen at the bottom of the pond and feel sorry for himself because he could neither sing nor jump.

Now one warm day as Tim Tadpole was wriggling in and out among the water lily plants, he met Mr. Turtle.

"Where are you going, Mr. Turtle?" asked Tim.

"To sit in the Sun," said Mr. Turtle. And then UP AND AWAY HE SWAM.

Then Miss Salamander came swimming by.

"Where are you going, Miss Salamander?" asked Tim.

"To sit in the Sun," said Miss Salamander, and up and away she swam.

Along came the Great Bullfrog.

"Oh, where are you going, Sir?" asked Tim.

"To sit in the Sun!" said the Great Bullfrog, and up and away he swam.

So Tim Tadpole followed after
the Great Bullfrog. Up and up
swam the Great Bullfrog and up
and up swam Tim. But the
Great Bullfrog climbed up on
the mossy bank and poor Tim
could not follow after him
because he had no legs and no
arms to climb with.

Tim Tadpole was left alone
with only the snails and little
fishes and they were not his
friends.

So now every day, all day long
Tim Tadpole felt sorry for himself because he could not find
the Sun. And every night all
night long Tim felt sorry for
himself because he could neither
jump nor sing.

One evening just after day and just before night as Tim Tadpole lay in the mud doing nothing whatever but feeling sorry for himself, along came the Great Bullfrog.

"Jump—come jump!" said the Great Bullfrog.

"I can't jump and I can't sing and I can't find the Sun," said Tim and he began to cry.

"What can you do?" asked the Great Bullfrog.

"Swim, just swim," said Tim.

"Then swim!" said the Great Bullfrog, and away he went.

So all day long Tim swam and
he swam. And all night long Tim
swam and he swam. And he never
had time to feel sorry for himself at all. Until one day what
should Tim find kicking out near
his tail but two little legs! Then
soon came a day when Tim had
a left arm and then came a day
when he had a right arm!
And every day Tim's tail was
getting shorter and shorter and
his mouth was growing wider
and wider.

"Now," said Tim, "I will find the Sun!"

Up crawled Tim out of the pond into the air, BUT—there was a strange creature looking for his supper—down came his big bill and SPLASH back into the pond slid Tim. And away he swam from the Great Blue Heron JUST IN TIME!

Then at last came a day when Tim found he had no tail at all, no tail whatever. And his two arms and his two legs were big and strong. And then Tim knew he was no longer Tim Tadpole because he was TIM FROG!!

Up and up swam Tim. Up he climbed onto the top side of a water lily pad. And then Tim saw the great ball of a Sun, slipping down behind the tall trees.

"Sing-sing—sing-sing!" trilled the gay Peeper Frogs.

"I want-to-jump—I want-to-jump!" sang young Tim Frog in his little new voice.

"Then jump—come jump—and jump!" croaked the Great Bull-frog. And—TIM JUMPED!!

Marjorie Flack

Mrs. Goose's Rubbers

One day Mrs. Goose could not find her rubbers. She looked in the same old place in the dark hall closet, and she looked under the bed, and she looked on the back porch; but she could not see them. So she went to Mrs. Pig's house and knocked at the door. When Mrs. Pig came to see who was knocking, Mrs. Goose said: "Have you seen my rubbers?"

"Of course I haven't seen your
rubbers, Mrs. Goose," Mrs. Pig
told her. "They wouldn't be over
here at my house, would they?"

"I don't know," said Mrs.
Goose. "I just thought they might
be."

Then she went to Mrs.
Squirrel's house and knocked at
the door. When Mrs. Squirrel
came to let her in, Mrs. Goose
said, "I just came to see if you
had seen my rubbers."

Mrs. Squirrel was making a nut-patty pudding. "No, indeed, I haven't seen your rubbers," she said. "Did you think they were here?"

"I didn't know," said Mrs. Goose. "I just thought they might be."

Then Mrs. Goose went home. She looked under the stove. She looked behind the door. She looked up on the clock shelf. She looked in the waste paper basket. She looked in the ice-box. But she could not find her rubbers.

Just then Mrs. Sheep went by.

"Oh, Mrs. Sheep," called Mrs. Goose, "have you seen my rubbers?"

Mrs. Sheep stopped by the fence. "Why, no, I haven't seen your rubbers," she said. "Where do you keep them?"

"In their same old place in the dark hall closet," said Mrs. Goose. "But they are not there."

Mrs. Sheep thought for a long minute, and then she said, "Why do you want your rubbers, anyway, Mrs. Goose? The sun is shining."

"Well, it just might rain tomorrow," Mrs. Goose said, "and then I'd want them."

"That's right," said Mrs. Sheep. "Come to think of it, I don't know where my rubbers are, either. I'd better go home and look them up." And she hurried on.

Still Mrs. Goose could not find her rubbers. She looked in the teakettle. She looked on the back stairs. She looked in the bread box. She looked under her pillow. And then she got a ladder and climbed up on the roof and stared all around. But her black eyes did not see her rubbers anywhere.

"Dear me, dear me," she said, "where can my rubbers be?"

Then she ate her supper and went to bed. Next morning when she woke up, rain was coming down—drip, drip, drip, on the roof. "Oh, it is raining today," said Mrs. Goose, "and I've got to go to market, and I haven't found my rubbers, and I'll get my poor feet all wet!"

She got up and made her bed and ate her breakfast. She dusted her house, and then she just had to go to market. The rain was coming down in big splashes, and there were puddles all over the sidewalk.

"I must find my rubbers!" said Mrs. Goose to herself. And she looked and looked in all the same places, but she did not find them. "Well," she said, "I shall have to go without them. That's what!" And she put on her coat and her hat, took her big green umbrella from its place in the dark hall closet, and started out.

She shut the door behind her, locked it with the tiny key, and stepped out on her porch. Then she put up her big green umbrella.

"Plop! Plop!" Two big some-things hit her on the head and almost knocked her hat off. They fell down on the porch behind her. "What can they be?" said Mrs. Goose to herself. She turned around and looked. There were her rubbers!

"I must have put them inside my umbrella," said Mrs. Goose. "Oh, now I remember! I put them there so they would not be lost. But it would have been better if I had put them back in their same place, in the dark hall closet."

Then she put her rubbers on, and went splashing along through the puddles on her way to market.

Miriam Clark Potter

Piggy

There once was a pig
Who was not very big,
   Not as big as he could be.
"Oink, oink," said the pig,
"I don't care a fig.
   I'm just as big as me."

Now this pig was wise
In the matter of size,
   For surely it's better to be
Just a pig of that size,
Since very few flies
   Can sit on his tail, you see.

Robert C. Glenn

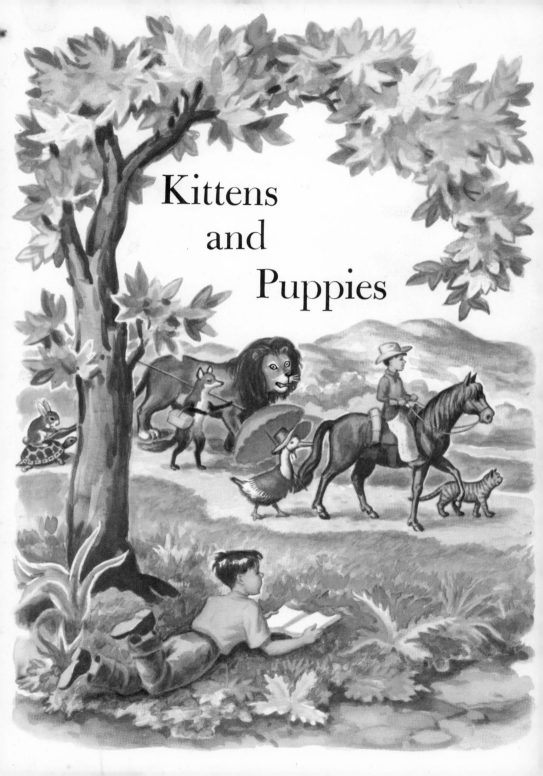

Kittens
and
Puppies

About Charlie

Once upon a time there was a dog named Charlie and a boy named Christopher.

And this story is about how Christopher got Charlie and about how Charlie got his name.

When he was a puppy, Charlie didn't have a name. He lived in a pet shop with a lot of other puppies. Every day people stopped to look in the pet shop window.

People like to watch puppies play.

And puppies like to be people's pets.

So when people looked in, the puppies wiggled and wagged and rolled over and sat up, and barked, "Yip-Yip. Buy me." All except Charlie.

Charlie just hid in the straw and peeped out at the people and watched and waited. He wanted to choose the one who would buy him for a pet. Charlie was a choosy puppy.

One day a lady stopped to look in the pet shop window and watch the puppies play.

And the puppies began to show
off. They wagged and wiggled
and yipped. All except Charlie.
Charlie just hid in the straw and
watched and waited.

A Cocker Spaniel sat up on
his hind legs and held up his
front paws. He looked so
longingly at the lady that she
said, "You darling dog. I'd like
to buy you." And she went into
the pet shop.

Charlie just hid deeper in the
straw and watched and waited.
He did not want a lady to buy
him. Ladies just held you in
their laps. Charlie wanted to run
and play. He wanted a boy to
buy him. So he hid deeper in the
straw.

"You don't have to hide," said
the Cocker Spaniel. "The lady is
not going to buy you. She is
going to buy me."

And she did.

Next door to the pet shop,
there was a shoemaker's shop.
One day Christopher came along.
He was taking his shoes to the
shoemaker's to be mended.

He stopped to look in the pet shop window.

Charlie was peeping out from the straw, waiting and watching, waiting and watching. When he saw Christopher, he jumped up and ran to the front of the window.

The dog looked at the boy.

The boy looked at the dog.

Then Christopher said, "Oh, oh! I wish I had a dog like you." And Charlie wiggled and wagged and yipped, "Buy me— please buy me. I've been waiting and watching for a boy like you."

"I want you for my pet," said Christopher.

"I want to take you home."

Christopher went into the pet shop.

The pet shop keeper knew which pup he wanted. For Charlie was wiggling and wagging and yipping.

"I want that puppy," said Christopher. "And that puppy wants me. How much does he cost?"

"I'll sell him cheap," said the pet shop keeper. "He growls at people and hides in the straw. You can have him for five dollars."

"I don't have any money," said Christopher. "But I'll buy him somehow. I'll be back."

Christopher patted Charlie. "You just wait, fellow. I'll be back with the money. You just wait."

So after that Charlie just waited. He didn't watch any more. He just waited. He knew that Christopher would be back.

Christopher went on to the shoemaker's shop. He had almost forgotten that he was taking his shoes to be mended.

"Well, my boy," said the shoemaker, "your shoes need
mending again. You must do a
lot of running and playing."

"I do," said Christopher, "and
I want a dog to run and play
with me. There is one in the pet
shop window that I want. He
wants me, too. But I do not have
the money to buy him."

"Why don't you earn the
money?" said the shoemaker.

"Could I?" said Christopher.
"How?"

"I need a boy to deliver
shoes," said the shoemaker.

"I can do it," said Christopher.
"And I'll work hard to earn the
money. Then I can buy that
puppy."

And Christopher did work
hard.

One day passed. Another day
passed.

Every day after school he
delivered shoes for the shoemaker.

Every day the shoemaker gave
him fifty cents.

And every day Christopher
looked in the pet shop window
to see if Charlie was still there.

Every day Christopher would
tap on the pet shop window
with his fifty cents. And Charlie
would wiggle and wag and yip,
"I'll wait. I won't let anyone else
buy me."

And he didn't.

So the boy worked and the dog
waited. Then one day Christopher
came running down the street.
He was shouting,

"Hooray! Hooray!
Tomorrow's the day."

He tapped on the pet shop window with the fifty cents he had just earned. "This makes four dollars and fifty cents," he shouted. "After work tomorrow I'll have five dollars—enough to buy you."

"Tomorrow's the day.
Hooray! Hooray!"

Charlie did not really know why Christopher was so happy. But the puppy was happy because the boy was happy. So Charlie wagged and wiggled and yipped, "I'll wait! I'll wait!"
"Good-by," said Christopher. "Remember, tomorrow you go home with me."

The next morning, early,
Christopher's mother came to
Christopher's room and woke
him.

He jumped out of bed shouting,

"Hooray! Hooray!
Today's the day."

"Look at your face," said
Mother. "It's covered with red
spots. You had better get back in
bed. I'll call Doctor Charles. You
probably have chickenpox or
something."

She handed Christopher a looking glass. "Here, look at yourself." Then she went to call the doctor.

Christopher looked at his face in the looking glass.

Sure enough, there were red spots all over it.

Soon Doctor Charles came.

"You have chickenpox, Christopher, my boy. You will have to stay in bed for a while," said Doctor Charles.

"Not today! Not today!" cried Christopher. "I can't stay in bed today. I can't stay in bed today."

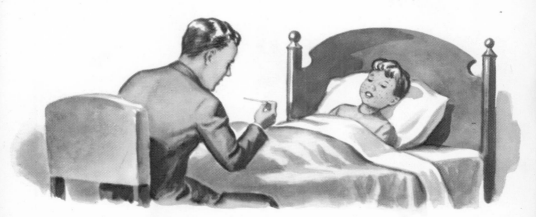

"Why not?" asked Doctor Charles.

"Today is the day that I earn enough money to buy my puppy. He is waiting for me. He won't know what has happened."

Christopher began to cry.

"Let me have the money you have earned," said Doctor Charles. "I'll see what I can do about it. I'll fix it. That is what doctors are for, to fix things."

So that day, when Charlie
came out from under the straw
he saw Doctor Charles. But when
Doctor Charles went into the pet
shop, Charlie went back under
the straw. He did not know that
Doctor Charles was going to take
him to Christopher. He thought
Dr. Charles was going to buy
him. So when the pet shop
keeper picked him up and
handed him to Doctor Charles,
Charlie growled and wiggled and
kicked.

"I'll have to put him in a
basket," said the pet shop
keeper. "He is putting up a
fight. This puppy has picked the
boy he wants and he does not
want anyone else to buy him."

"I'm going to take him to the boy he wants," said Doctor Charles.

"But he does not know that," said the pet shop keeper.

And Charlie did not know that the doctor was taking him to Christopher. He just knew that he could not get out of the basket. The doctor had put the basket in the back seat of his car. And Charlie knew that he was getting farther and farther away from the pet shop. Now he wouldn't be in the pet shop when Christopher came to get him. Charlie soon began to bark and whimper.

Soon the car stopped. The doctor got out and said, "Just a minute, fellow. I must stop here. Then I'll take you to Christopher."

But Charlie did not understand. He just barked and whimpered and tried to get out of the basket.

Some children were playing on the side-walk. They heard Charlie and looked into the car.

"What's in the basket?" "Is it a dog?"

"Let's see." "Open the basket."
"Let's look."

The children opened the basket
. . . AND . . .

Out jumped Charlie.

Away he ran, with all of the
children after him.

"Hurry! Hurry! Catch him!
Catch him!"

The children ran fast—but
Charlie ran faster.

"We can get him," shouted the children. "Run! Run!"

"Faster! Faster! We'll get him."

"No, you won't," barked Charlie.

"Yip-yip, yip-yip." Up one street, down another.

"Faster . . . faster!"

The children ran fast—but Charlie ran faster.

When Dr. Charles came out
of the house and got into his
car, he saw the empty basket. "I
will have to find that pup," he
said to himself. "I told
Christopher I'd fix things for
him and I will."

The doctor drove around
town . . . around and around the
town. At last he saw the
children. They were chasing the
puppy.

Poor Charlie was slowing
down. He was getting tired.

The doctor stopped his car.

Soon a tired little puppy
found himself back in the basket.

But this time the basket was
in the front seat where Dr.
Charles could watch it. Dr.
Charles drove straight to
Christopher's house. And he
took the basket straight up to
Christopher's room.

Christopher said, "Thank you,
Doctor Charles. You fixed things
for me. Now I'm going to name
my dog after you. I'll call him
Charlie."

"Good!" said Doctor Charles.

"How did you get him?" asked
Christopher. "I needed fifty cents
more. I was going to earn it
today . . . delivering shoes for
the shoemaker."

"I fixed that, too," said the
doctor. "I delivered shoes."

"Oh, thanks," said Christopher.
"You fixed things. You fixed
things just fine."

"I'll fix that chickenpox, too,"
said Doctor Charles.

Soon all the red spots went
away,
And Christopher went out to
play.
And after that . . . Hooray!
Hooray!
He played with Charlie every
day.

So that's how a boy named
Christopher got a dog named
Charlie.

Inez Hogan

Kitten Talk

I'm purring because
  I feel so fine.
I'm purring because
  This ball is mine.
I'm purring because
  I've cleaned my fur.
And anyway,
  I like to purr.

Clara Ellen Spelman

Wonderful Willy

Willy was a little brown dog. He lived with the Smith family.

Mr. Smith was very nice to Willy.

Mrs. Smith was very nice to Willy.

And the Smith boy, Harold, was nicer to Willy than anyone.

So Willy should have been very happy.

But he was not happy.

He saw that Mr. Smith did not walk around on four legs.

He walked on two legs.

So did Mrs. Smith.

And so did Harold Smith.

Willy wanted to walk on just his two hind legs too.

He tried and tried to walk on just his hind legs.

And at last Willy did!

Mr. Smith saw Willy walking on his hind legs.

"How wonderful Willy is!" said Mr. Smith.

"How wonderful Willy is!" said Mrs. Smith.

"How VERY wonderful Willy is!" shouted Harold Smith.

The Smiths were very proud of Willy.

They called in their friends
and neighbors, to see Willy
walking around the living room
on his hind legs. It was hard
work for Willy to walk around
on his hind legs. But he didn't
mind, because he was so proud
and happy.

One day the Smiths were
shopping on Main Street. Willy
walked with them, on his hind
legs.

Everybody who came along stopped to look at the way Willy walked on two legs. They all thought he was wonderful.

Just then the kind butcher came out of his shop, and put some bones down on the sidewalk for the dogs.

Dogs came running from everywhere. Old dogs, young dogs, black dogs, white dogs, brown dogs, yellow dogs and spotted dogs. Even a little puppy who wasn't old enough to eat a bone, scampered toward the butcher shop.

Willy tried to run on his hind
legs. But he couldn't. He could
only walk slowly.

He wanted a bone so much
that at last he dropped down
on all four legs and RAN.

It felt so good to be on four
legs again that Willy ran faster
than he had ever run before. He
ran so fast that he reached the
butcher shop first and picked out
the biggest, juiciest bone of all.

When Willy had eaten his
bone and started back to the
Smiths, he remembered how
proud of him Mr. Smith had
been, when he walked on just
his hind legs.

Willy remembered how proud
Mrs. Smith had been.

He remembered how very
proud Harold Smith had been.

Poor Willy thought the Smiths
would be ashamed of him
because he had stopped walking
on two legs and had run on all
four.

And right on Main Street in
front of all their friends too!

Willy walked very slowly
with his tail between his legs.
He felt very unhappy.

But when Mr. Smith saw
Willy he said, "How wonderful
Willy is, he can walk on just
his hind legs when he wants to.
But when he wants to go fast
he can run faster than any
other dog on all four legs."

"How wonderful Willy is!" said
Mrs. Smith too.

"How VERY wonderful Willy
is!" shouted Harold Smith.

And Mr. Smith, Mrs. Smith and Harold Smith felt prouder of Willy than ever.

And from that day on, when Willy walked on his two hind legs, he felt happy.

When he ran on all four legs, he felt happy.

But when he just sat by the fire with Harold Smith, he felt VERY happy.

Tony Brice

My Puppy

Round and round
And in and out—
(I wonder what
It's all about!
He doesn't stop
For this or that;
He doesn't tease
The sleepy cat.
He doesn't hear me
When I call;
He doesn't try
To eat his ball.
I thought he had
A little sense;
I guess it must
Have been pretense.)
You make me dizzy!
Stop, I say—
Or else go round
The other way!   *Verna Hills*

How They Walk

When elephants walk,
They walk like this:
Clump—clump—clump.
They're very heavy and very
    slow.
This is the way that elephants
    go:
Clump—clump—clump.

When kitty-cats walk,
They walk like this:
Pitpat—pitpat—pitpat.
They're soft as silk, and
    elegant—
Not at all like an elephant.
Pitpat—pitpat—pitpat.

Grace Olin Jordan

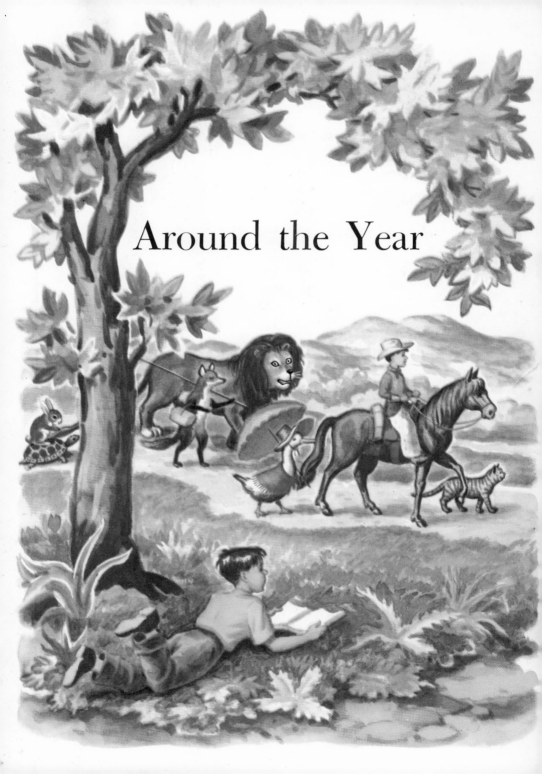

Around the Year

Sliding

We can slide
  down the hill
    or
      down the stair
or
  down the street
    or anywhere

or
  down the roof
    where the shingles broke,

or
  down the trunk
    of the back-yard oak,
      down the slide
        or the ice
          or the slippery street.

We can slide
on our sled
on our skates
on our feet.

Oh, it's lots of fun to go outside
and slide
and SLIDE
and SLIDE
and SLIDE.

Myra Cohn

Picnic Woods

A sunny day in May is a perfect day for picnics. So Mister Fox packed his picnic basket. A sunny day in May is a fine day for fishing, too. So Mister Fox took his fishing pole and his picnic basket and started off.

As he went through the woods he didn't see two gray squirrels up in a tree . . . but the two gray squirrels saw him. And they followed him to the river.

When Mister Fox reached his
favorite fishing place he put his
basket behind an old elm tree.
Then he dropped his line into
the water wondering what he
would catch . . . and the two
gray squirrels watched him. As
they watched they wondered
what was in his picnic basket.
They tiptoed to the elm tree.
They tiptoed to the basket.

"Today is a perfect picnic
day," whispered one squirrel.
"And here is a basket to take to
a picnic." The two gray squirrels
tiptoed away from the old elm
tree carrying the basket between
them.

They ran away from Mister
Fox.

They ran away from the river.

They ran away WITH the
picnic basket.

As they ran through the
woods they didn't see an old
raccoon by a dead oak tree . . .
but the old raccoon saw them.

The old raccoon stopped the
squirrels. He lifted the cover to
look in the basket. Then he
took the basket. The two gray
squirrels felt very sad but there
was nothing that they could do.

"Today is a perfect picnic day, and this is the basket I will take to my picnic," said the old raccoon as he went away.

The old raccoon laughed as he left the squirrels.

He laughed as he carried the picnic basket.

He laughed as he went through the woodland.

He hopped and he skipped and he didn't see the bear that was hiding behind a tree . . . but the bear saw him.

The bear snatched the basket from the hands of the old raccoon. He held it over his head and said: "Today is a perfect picnic day. Now I have a basket to take to a picnic."

The old raccoon felt very sad. But there was nothing that he could do.

The bear took the picnic basket and walked farther into the woods. While he walked he said:

"I am the strongest animal in the woodland. I am the biggest animal in the woodland. I have the picnic basket now and no one shall take it from me."

He looked at the basket and he looked all around. But he didn't look down at the ground . . . and his foot slipped into a rabbit hole. The bear fell down. The basket flew up and when it came down a brown bunny caught it and pulled it into his underground house.

The bear felt very sad but there was nothing that he could do. The bunny felt very glad. This was a perfect picnic day and he had the basket now. "Who wants a picnic underground? Not me!" thought the bunny.

The bunny ran through a long tunnel.

Then he ran through a short tunnel.

And when he came to the end of it he went up through a rabbit hole in another part of the woods, far away from the bear.

As he climbed up, he didn't see the beavers near by cutting down a tree . . . but the beavers saw him.

They took the picnic basket and went into the river.

The beavers swam through the river.

They swam to their lodge.

They swam away with the picnic basket.

The brown bunny felt very sad
but there was nothing that he
could do.

The beavers put the basket on
top of their lodge and said:

"Today is a perfect day, but
we must finish our work before
we eat. The basket will be safe
here in the middle of the river."

The beavers left the lodge
and didn't see the little water
rat family . . . but the water
rats saw them.

When the beavers had gone
the water rats came out, and
the oldest of them said:

"There is enough food here to
last us all day. Today is a
perfect picnic day and this
basket will be our boat." The
water rats pushed the basket
into the water with a splash.

They sailed away from the
beavers' lodge.

They sailed away down stream.

They sailed away WITH the
picnic basket.

They sailed away and away
and didn't see Mister Fox who
was fishing by the elm tree . . .
but Mister Fox saw them.

"MY PICNIC BASKET," cried
Mister Fox. And he caught it
with his fishing pole just in
time for lunch. Mister Fox pulled
his basket up on shore. Mister
Fox unpacked his picnic basket.
And he said, as he ate his
lunch:

"Today IS a perfect picnic day
and a fine day for fishing, too."

Lilian Robertson

Hello and Good-bye

Hello and Good-bye
Met today,
And this is what
I heard them say:

"Hello, Good-bye."
"Hello, Hello."
"Good-bye, Good-bye."
"Good-bye, Hello."

James Steel Smith

Pets in School

The first graders loved their little country school. Every day they played under the tree.

And every day Bonnie tried to decide which she liked best—the playhouse, the special first-grade recess, the stories that Miss Cora read every morning, or the story that she was learning to read from her own book. One morning Miss Cora brought a cage that she had made of very fine wire. Then Bonnie decided that she liked this best of all.

The cage was like a box. It had a board for a floor, and a door in one end.

The first graders crowded around it.

"What's it for?" the first graders asked Miss Cora.

"It's to put things in," said Miss Cora. "I want you to bring something to live in it."

"Something alive?" asked Davy.

"Something wild?" asked Bonnie.

"Something that crawls?" asked Jimmy.

"Something that flies?" asked Mary.

"Something alive," said Miss
Cora. "Something wild. It may
run or crawl or fly or walk.
Look for something alive as you
come to school across the fields
or through the woods. The woods
and the fields are full of wild
things. Whole families sometimes
live on a little piece of grass.
Whenever you walk through the
woods, bright eyes are looking at
you from almost every tree. And
whenever you step, you may be
stepping on somebody's house.
Let's ask Davy to bring something for our cage tomorrow."

The next morning Davy came
running through the woods with
his hands held tightly.

"I've got something, Miss
Cora!" he shouted when he was
still a long way off. "Open the
cage door and let me put him in.
He's crawling around in my
hands. Ouch, he tickles!"

Bonnie ran and opened the cage door. Everybody crowded around to see. Davy held his hands to the cage door, opened them, and out flew a ladybug. Bonnie slammed the door shut.

Soon it was eight o'clock, and time for Chris to ring the bell. At once the ladybug set out to explore the cage.

When the first grade finished
reading their lesson, they drew
pictures of the ladybug. Bonnie
drew a ladybug as big as her
hand. She made thirteen spots
on his wings. She gave him
three pairs of long, crooked
legs, and a pair of short, crooked
feelers.

At recess the first graders put
twigs and leaves inside the
ladybug's cage. Then they
watched him as he crawled over
and under the leaves and up
and down the twigs.

"He is trying to find his home," said Bonnie.

"Ladybugs do not have any home," Miss Cora said. "They are always on the go."

The boys and girls left the ladybug in the cage when they went home that night. The next morning when Jimmy opened the cage door to put a fresh twig inside, the ladybug spread his tiny wings and flew straight out the open window.

Until eight o'clock, when the
bell rang, the first graders
looked for him. Over and over
they sang:

"Ladybug, ladybug,
  Fly away home.
  Your house is on fire,
  And your children do roam!"

But the ladybug never flew
back. Miss Cora said he would
be safe. She said that he would
fly into the woods. Then when
winter came, he would crawl
down under the dry leaves
where it was warm, and stay
until spring. When his work was
done in the spring, he would die.

133

"Maybe Jimmy will bring something for our cage tomorrow," Miss Cora said.

The next morning Jimmy hurried to school carrying something in his cap.

"Open the cage door!" he shouted when he was still a long way off. "So I can put him in!"

Bonnie ran and opened the door. Jimmy held his cap close. Out tumbled a Daddy Longlegs.

When he could straighten out
his eight tangled legs, Daddy
Longlegs ran as fast as he could
into a corner. With the middle
part of his long legs high in the
air, and his little body hanging
low between them, he looked as
if he were walking on four pairs
of stilts.

The first graders drew his
picture. Then at recess they went
to the woods to hunt food for
him. Miss Cora said he especially
liked baby spiders and little
insects.

But Daddy Longlegs wanted to find his own lunch. When he saw that Mary had forgotten to shut the door tight, he scampered out of the cage. As the children came out of the woods, Bonnie saw Daddy Long-legs hurry down the wall and under the schoolhouse.

They looked everywhere for him, but they could not find him.

"The day of the first hard frost, he will likely die," Miss Cora said. "His work will be finished. Next spring you can find his children in the grass. I wonder what Mary will bring for our cage tomorrow."

The next morning Mary came
to school carrying a glass jar in
her hands. Bonnie ran to open
the door of the cage. Jimmy
and Davy and Miss Cora came
to watch.

Mary lifted the lid of the
jar, and into the cage flew a
beautiful big butterfly, all yellow
and black, rimmed with blue,
and with an orange ball on her
hind wings.

"Oh!" said Bonnie. "She's
pretty!"

"She is really beautiful,"
said Miss Cora. "She is all
dressed up. Do you suppose she
is going to a party?"

"Let's call her Cinderella,"
said Bonnie. And they did.

137

After their reading lesson, the
first graders drew Cinderella's
picture. And at recess they got
twigs for her to rest on, and
some goldenrod from which to
drink nectar. When they went
home at night, they made sure
the door of the cage was shut so
that Cinderella could not fly
away.

But the next morning when
they went to school, they found
Cinderella lying still in a corner
of the cage. Her beautiful wings
were folded stiffly.

"Butterflies always die when their work is finished," Miss Cora said. "But somewhere on the leaf of a tree or a twig, Cinderella laid some eggs. You'll see her children next year. And now, let's see what Bonnie will bring for our cage tomorrow."

The next morning on the way to school Bonnie walked behind the other boys and girls.

"Why don't you walk faster?"
asked Chris. "We won't have
time to play before the bell
rings, if you don't hurry."

"I'm looking for something
special for the cage," said
Bonnie.

"A bee?" asked Debby. "I see
a bee."

"I don't want anything that
flies," said Bonnie. "I want it to
stay in the cage."

"A squirrel?" asked Emmy. "I see a squirrel."

"I don't want anything that runs fast," said Bonnie.

"Another butterfly?" asked Althy. "We could find another butterfly."

"I don't want anything that dies so quickly," said Bonnie. "I want something that lives a long time."

"Something that doesn't fly, something that doesn't run, and something that lives a long time. There isn't any such animal," said Chris.

"Anyway," said Bonnie, "I'm looking for one. You never can tell what you'll find in the woods. Miss Cora said so."

Down the road they went.
Bonnie walked slowly behind
the others. She looked this way
and that way for something
special.

At the crossroads Jimmy
waited for them. At the bend in
the road Mary met them. And
at the footbridge waited Davy.

They were all on the footbridge before Bonnie reached it.
She stood and looked this way
and that way. She looked
through the woods and up and
down the river bank. She
hoped to see a little animal
running through the grass, or
hiding on the gray bark of a
tree.

Suddenly she opened her eyes
wide. Up the hill near the path
she saw just what she was
looking for. It couldn't fly. It
couldn't run. Bonnie did not
know how old it was, but she
was sure that it was not going
to die tomorrow.

She stood quietly in the path
and waited. It was coming
toward her, very slowly. Closer
and closer it crawled on its
four big feet. It had a thick
head, and carried a brown house
on its back. Its eyes were little
and red. Up the hill it crawled
and then straight across the
path in front of Bonnie. It was
a big turtle.

Bonnie reached down and
touched it with her finger.

Quick as a wink he pulled his legs inside his house.

Then he jerked in his neck and his thick head.

"Hiss!" he said. Then he closed the door of his house.

Bonnie picked him up, took her first reader out of her book-bag and put the turtle in. Then she hurried to school.

"I've found something for the cage!" she shouted when she came near the schoolhouse.

The boys and girls crowded around her, but Bonnie walked straight to the front of the schoolroom. She put her hand in her bookbag, pulled out the turtle, and laid him on Miss Cora's desk.

"He is a very old turtle," said
Miss Cora. "He may be a
hundred years old."

"Let's name him Grandpap,"
said Bonnie.

So they named him Grandpap.

Bonnie put him into the cage,
shut the door, and went away.
Then Grandpap opened the door
of his house, and stuck out his
thick head.

After their reading lesson,
the first graders drew a picture
of his brown house, first with
his feet and head outside of it,
and then with his feet and
head inside and the door shut.

146

Every morning the children brought Grandpap nuts from the woods and tomatoes from their gardens at home. They caught flies for him, and found long, fat worms that he liked best of all.

At first Grandpap only sat and looked at the food.

"Your dinner is ready, Grandpap," said the children. But Grandpap ate his dinner when he pleased.

One day Bonnie offered Grandpap a bite of melon. He crawled up and ate it from her hand. After that, every day he had melon for dessert.

At recess the first graders took Grandpap out on the playground with them. When they played house, they let him sit in the corner in the sun and doze, since he was Grandpap.

At noon they sometimes played "Whoopyhide." Once they saw Grandpap go through the fence into the meadow. They shut their eyes and pretended that he was hiding. Then they climbed the fence and found him in the grass, and brought him back again.

Every day after that they
played "Whoopyhide" with Grandpap. Sometimes he just walked
in the sun. Sometimes he dozed,
his head hanging out of his
house. Sometimes he went into
his house and closed the door.
The children could not see him
there.

One bright day when Grandpap was walking around in the
sun, the first graders shut their
eyes and told him to run and
hide.

In a few minutes, they opened
their eyes and ran to look for
him. They looked all around
the tree. But Grandpap was not
there.

They looked along the fence,
but Grandpap was not there.

They climbed the fence and
looked in the field. But
Grandpap was not there.

They looked along the edge of
the woods. But Grandpap was
not there. They walked through
the leaves and around the roots
of trees. But Grandpap was not
to be seen.

Then all the children began
to look for Grandpap. In and out
of fence corners, up and down
the playground, across the field
and through the woods they
went, looking and calling. But
there was not a sign of Grandpap.

"Has he gone away to die?"
asked Bonnie. Tears hurt her
eyes.

"Not Grandpap!" said Miss Cora. "He's gone to find a sunny place in the woods where he can dig himself a deep hole and go to sleep for the winter. In the spring, when the days are long and warm, you may see an old log some day, and there will be twenty turtles on it. One of them will be Grandpap."

"But how will I know which is Grandpap?" asked Bonnie.

Miss Cora thought a minute.

"He will be the first on the log, I think," she said. "Because, you see, that's where Grandpap belongs."

Rebecca Caudill

The Animals' Christmas Tree

One Christmas day a sparrow flew down to a window sill. He cocked his little brown head and peeped into the window. Then he called a friend in a tree near by.

"Come quick! Come quick!"

"What is it?" asked the other sparrow. And he flew down beside him.

"Just look in this window. There is a tree growing in the house!" said the first sparrow.

"How queer!" said the other sparrow.

"It is not like our trees in the woods," said the first sparrow. "Look at all the pretty things on it."

Just then some children came running into the room. They ran at once to the tree. Father and Mother came in, too.

The sparrows watched and listened. They heard the children laughing and talking. They saw them get presents right from the tree.

"That is a lovely kind of tree," said the first sparrow. "They say that it is a Christmas tree. I wish we could have one like it in the woods."

"Perhaps we can," said the other sparrow. "Let us ask King Lion if we may have a Christmas tree."

"Good!" said the first sparrow.

So they flew away to find King Lion.

They told him what they had
seen. "The children are having a
Christmas tree," said the little
sparrows. "Why can't animals
have a Christmas tree, too?"

"We can," said King Lion.
"But we must hurry, for
Christmas Day will soon be over.
I will call the animals together
at once."

So King Lion roared as loud
as he could. All the animals
heard him roaring and they came
to see what he wanted. All the
birds came, too.

When they were all there,
King Lion raised his paw. This
meant that everyone must be
quiet. Then he said, "Sparrow,
tell the animals what you have
seen."

The little sparrow told what he
had seen. "The tree was full of
presents," he said. "Each child
had something that he liked. It
was something that looked pretty
on the tree. Wouldn't it be nice
for us to have a Christmas tree
with presents on it?"

The animals clapped their
paws and each one said, "Yes,
yes, yes!" as loud as he could.

King Lion raised his paw
again, to tell them to be quiet.
Then he said, "Every animal who
wishes to have a Christmas
tree, please raise his right paw."

Every right paw was raised.

"When shall we have the Christmas tree?" asked King Lion.

"Now! Now!" said all the animals.

"Where shall we have it?" asked King Lion.

"Here!" said all the animals.

"This little pine tree is as tall as the Christmas tree that we saw," said the sparrows. "It will be lovely when we decorate it and put on the presents."

"Who will decorate it?" asked King Lion.

"I will decorate it," said the giraffe. "I am so tall I can reach up to the tiptop of this pine tree."

"We will make lights for it," said the fireflies. "We will shine as bright as little candles."

"I will be policeman and keep good order," said the bulldog.

"Now we must decide on the presents," said King Lion. "Each animal may say what he wants and Mr. Owl will write it down."

So Mr. Owl got out his book and his pen. Every time the lion told him to write down a present, he said, "Whoo? Whoo?" so he would be sure to put down the right name.

"Now remember," said King Lion, "we want a beautiful tree and a happy time. Ask for a present that will look pretty on the tree. And do not ask for anything to hurt another animal."

"King Lion," said Miss Cat, "when we first talked about having a Christmas tree, I made up my mind to ask for a little mouse, but the mouse would not like that. So I shall ask for a bowl of cream."

"Good!" said King Lion. "Mr. Owl, write down a bowl of cream for Miss Cat."

"Whoo? Whoo?" said Mr. Owl, and he wrote down the name and the present.

Then Mr. Fox said, "I was
going to ask for a fat chicken,
but the chicken would not like
that. So I will take a bunch of
grapes."

"Write down a bunch of grapes
for Mr. Fox," said King Lion.

"Whoo? Whoo?" said Mr. Owl,
and he wrote it down.

Mr. Tiger said, "I was going to
ask for a lamb, but the lamb
would not like that. So give me
a bunch of bananas."

"Write down a bunch of
bananas for Mr. Tiger," said
King Lion.

"Whoo? Whoo?" said Mr. Owl,
and he wrote it down.

Miss Monkey said, "I will take
a new swing."

Mr. Bulldog said, "I will take a new collar."

Mr. Giraffe said, "I will take a basket of red apples."

Mrs. Rabbit said, "I will take a carrot."

Mrs. Squirrel said, "I will take a bag of nuts."

Mr. Goat said, "I want the tablecloth off the line, but the maid would not like that. So I will take an ice-cream cone."

So it went on until they came to Mr. Pig. He said, "I want a bucket of pig wash."

"Oh, Mr. Pig!" said Miss Monkey. "That will not look pretty on the tree."

"King Lion said I could have what I want, and I want a bucket of pig wash."

"Why not take a pretty string of popcorn?" asked the tiger.

"I want a bucket of pig wash."

"Why not take a nice glass of milk?" asked the cat.

"I want a bucket of pig wash."

"Well," said King Lion, "we said that each one is to have what he wants. So, I suppose that he must have his bucket of pig wash."

Mr. Owl said, "Whoo? Whoo?"
But before he could write Mr.
Pig's name, Miss Cat jumped up.

She said, "If Mr. Pig has the
pig wash that he wants, I will
take a little mouse. That is what
I want."

Mr. Fox said, "If Mr. Pig has
the pig wash that he wants, I
will take a fat chicken. That is
what I want."

Mr. Tiger said, "If Mr. Pig has the pig wash that he wants, I will take a lamb. That is what I want."

Mr. Goat said, "If Mr. Pig has the pig wash that he wants, I will take the tablecloth. That is what I want."

Then King Lion raised his paw and all the animals were quiet.

He said, "I thought I would put on Santa Claus's clothes and give out the presents. But if everyone else takes what he wants, I will take what I want. I want a nice fat pig."

Mr. Pig began to squeal and tried to run away. But Mr. Bulldog, the policeman, caught him and brought him back.

Just then Mr. Owl said,
"Whoo? Whoo? You talked so
fast I could not write down what
you said. The last present I have
is an ice-cream cone for Mr.
Goat. You are next, Mr. Pig. Do
you want a bucket of pig wash?"

"No! no! no!" said Mr. Pig, as
loud as he could. "I don't want
a bucket of pig wash. I want a
watermelon."

"Oh!" said King Lion. "Then I will be Santa Claus and give the presents."

"I will take the bowl of cream," said Miss Cat.

"I will take the bunch of grapes," said Mr. Fox.

"I will take the bunch of bananas," said Mr. Tiger.

"I will take the ice-cream cone," said Mr. Goat.

"Very well," said King Lion. "Now get the things to put on the tree."

The animals got the things. Mr. Giraffe decorated the tree and put on the presents. The fireflies flew about and lighted it, just like candles. When all was ready, King Lion gave out the presents. He was dressed like Santa Claus. Each animal had something he liked, and each present looked pretty on the tree. And not one present hurt anyone.

So they all had a happy Christmas Day.

Rose L. Hardy and Geneva J. Hecox

The Moon

The moon is a cooky
White, frosted, and gay
That small hungry clouds
Soon nibble away.

Frances Gibson

Wee Robin's Christmas Song

It was Christmas Morning. Old Gray Pussy went out for a walk. She walked along the narrow path that ran alongside of the singing brook. Pussy knew that Wee Robin Redbreast made his home in the briar bush near the brook.

Old Gray Pussy had not gone very far when she saw Wee Robin Redbreast in the briar bush. Wee Robin was hopping about from twig to twig above her head.

"Good morning, Wee Robin," miaowed Gray Pussy, as she looked up at him. "And where are you going on this fine Christmas morning?"

Wee Robin twittered merrily:

I'm going to visit the King
   today.
Tra la la la la la!
To sing him a song for
   Christmas Day.
Tra la la la la la!

"I'd like to see the King, too," said Pussy, as she brushed her whiskers. "Don't be in such a hurry. Hop down a minute and I'll show you the bonnie white ring around my neck."

172

Wee Robin cocked his head to
one side, and looked down at
Gray Pussy. Then Wee Robin
sang:

I don't want to see your bonnie
   white ring.
No no no no no no no!
You tried to catch mousie, you'll
   never catch me.
Good-by, Pussy, now I must go.

And Wee Robin fluttered his wings and sang:

Tra la la la la la la!

And away he flew!

Wee Robin flew on and on, until he came to a high stone wall. He stopped there to rest, and saw Greedy Gray Hawk perched near him on the stone wall.

"Good morning, Wee Robin," said Greedy Gray Hawk. "And where are you going this fine Christmas morning?"

Wee Robin hopped farther
away from Greedy Gray Hawk.
Then he sang:

I'm going to visit the King
today.
Tra la la la la la!
To sing him a song for
Christmas Day.
Tra la la la la la!

"I'd like to see the King, too,"
said Greedy Gray Hawk. "You
sing so sweetly, Wee Robin. I
could listen to you all day.
Don't be in such a hurry. I'd
like to go with you. Won't you
come a little closer? I want to
show you the bonnie white
feather on the tip of my wing."

Wee Robin hopped still farther
away from Greedy Gray Hawk
before he trilled:

I don't want to see your feather
  of white.
No no no no no no no!
You pecked at a linnet, you'll
  not peck at me.
Good-by, Mister Hawk, I must
  go.

Wee Robin fluttered his wings
and sang:

　　Tra la la la la la la!

And away he flew!

After a while Wee Robin came to a snow-covered rock. The sun was warm there, so Wee Robin thought this would be a nice spot to rest. He did not know that old Sly Fox lived in a hole under the rock. But when he looked down old Sly Fox poked his head out and looked up at Wee Robin.

"Good morning, Wee Robin," said old Sly Fox. "What a treat it is to see you! And where are you going this fine Christmas morning?"

"Oh," said Wee Robin.

I'm going to visit the King
   today.
Tra la la la la la!
To sing him a song for
   Christmas Day.
Tra la la la la la!

"I'd like to see the King, too,"
said old Sly Fox. "Don't be in
such a hurry. I'd like to go with
you. Hop down a minute, Wee
Robin, and I'll show you the
bonnie white spot at the tip end
of my beautiful tail. No fox in
the whole country has a white
spot like mine."

"That may well be," replied
Wee Robin, and he sang loudly:

I don't want to see that bonnie
   white spot.
No no no no no no no!
You tried to get Lambie, you'll
   never get me.
Good-by, old Sly Fox, I must go.

Wee Robin spread his wings
and trilled:

Tra la la la la la la!

And away he flew!

Wee Robin flew through the cold quiet air. Soon he came to a stream. The sun spread a golden cover over the water and Wee Robin stopped for a drink. There on a fence, close to the brook, sat a boy. Boy was eating his lunch. Wee Robin perched on the fence and watched him.

"Good morning, Wee Robin," said Boy. "Where are you going?"

Again Wee Robin sang:

I'm going to visit the King
    today.
Tra la la la la la!
To sing him a song for
    Christmas Day.
Tra la la la la la!

"Come a little closer, Wee Robin. I'll let you have some of my bread crumbs."

Wee Robin hopped once, Wee Robin hopped twice, Wee Robin hopped three hops away from Boy. Then he sang:

I don't want your crumbs and I
   don't like you.
No no no no no no no!
You put little chickadee into a
   cage.
Good-by, naughty boy, I must go.

Wee Robin spread his wings and gaily trilled:

Tra la la la la la la!

And away he flew!

Away and away and away he
flew, until he reached the white
marble palace of the King. There
he perched on the branch of a
small fir tree that grew close to
the King's window, and sang as
though his tiny throat would
burst with joy:

Jingle jingle jingle bells,
All day I've been singing,
Jingle jingle jingle bells,
I have come a-winging,
Just to bring my Christmas song
I only want to say
Merry, Merry Christmas, King,
A happy Christmas Day.

"What a beautiful song," said
the King.

He called the Queen and they both stood still and listened.

"Never before have I heard such sweet singing," said the Queen.

"What shall we give Wee Robin for singing this lovely song?" asked the King.

"We can give him Jenny Wren for a wife," the Queen replied.

"You do think of the nicest things," said the King.

There was great rejoicing at the Court when Wee Robin and Jenny Wren were married in the garden outside of the King's palace.

The Queen gave a party and all the singing birds from the woods and fields came to dance at the wedding.

When the dancing was over, Wee Robin and Jenny Wren hopped to the King's window. They thanked the King and Queen for the lovely party and then, with a whir of wings, they both flew away.

On and on and on they flew. They flew over snow-covered cottages. They flew over powder-white trees. They flew over tall church steeples. They did not stop flying until they flew right into Wee Robin's nest in the briar bush.

Elsie-Jean

At Our House

Our Clock

Our clock is a little house on the
  wall,
And a cuckoo bird lives in it,
He tells the time at every hour,
Exactly on the minute.

When it is one, he says Cuckoo!
And Cuckoo! Cuckoo! when it's
  two.
And when it's three, he'll call
  for you,
Cuckoo! Cuckoo! Cuckoo!

Florence Eakman

Shutting Doors

The screen door
　　slaps,
the back door
　　plops,
the shed door
　　claps,
the front door
　　blops.

Of course, the sound (from less
　to more)
depends upon who shuts the
　door.

James Steel Smith

The Mitten Song

"Thumbs in the thumb-place,
Fingers all together!"
This is the song
We sing in mitten-weather.

When it is cold,
It doesn't matter whether
Mittens are wool,
Or made of finest leather.

This is the song
We sing in mitten-weather:
"Thumbs in the thumb-place,
Fingers all together!"

Marie Louise Allen

Grown-Up People

They like it sitting straight in
   chairs,
They like it talking quietly,
They like it walking down the
   stairs,
Instead of bump

             ing

                down

                   like

                     me.

Dorothy Aldis

Bad

I've been bad and I'm in bed
For the naughty things I said.

I'm in bed. I wish I had
Not said those things that were
   so bad.

I wish that I'd been good instead.
But I was bad. And I'm in bed.

Dorothy Aldis

The Stars

I like to go to bed and see
The stars on high look down on
  me.
They are so friendly and I know
They wink because they like me
  so.

Nancy A. Sigmund